ASTROLOGY CATS

COLORING BOOK

ILLUSTRATED BY
JEN RACINE

instagram: @jenracinecoloring

facebook.com/jenracinecoloring

www.jenracine.com

BOOKS BY JEN RACINE

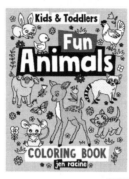

ETSY SHOP
WWW.ETSY.COM/SHOP/JENRACINECOLORING

Copyright © 2019 by Eclectic Esquire Media LLC
Published by Lake George Press

ISBN-13: 978-1-7336959-5-4

aries

taurus

gemini

cancer

leo

virgo

libra

scorpio

sagittarius

capricorn

aquarius

pisces

LEO

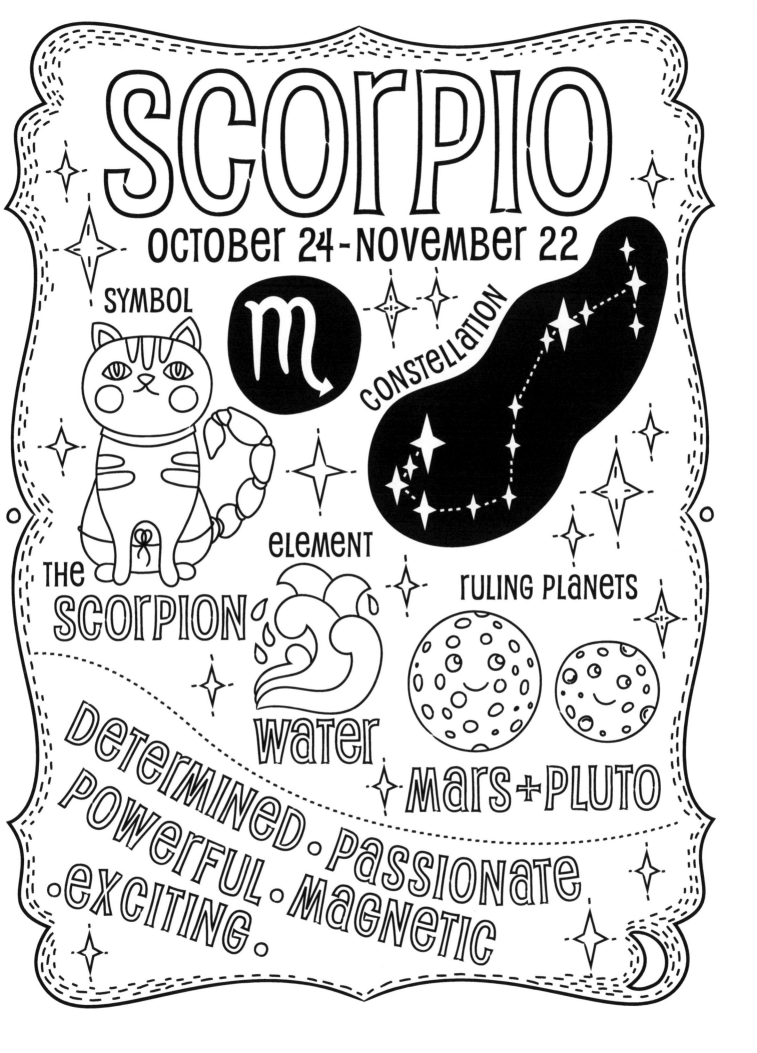

SAGITTARIUS

capricorn

PISCES

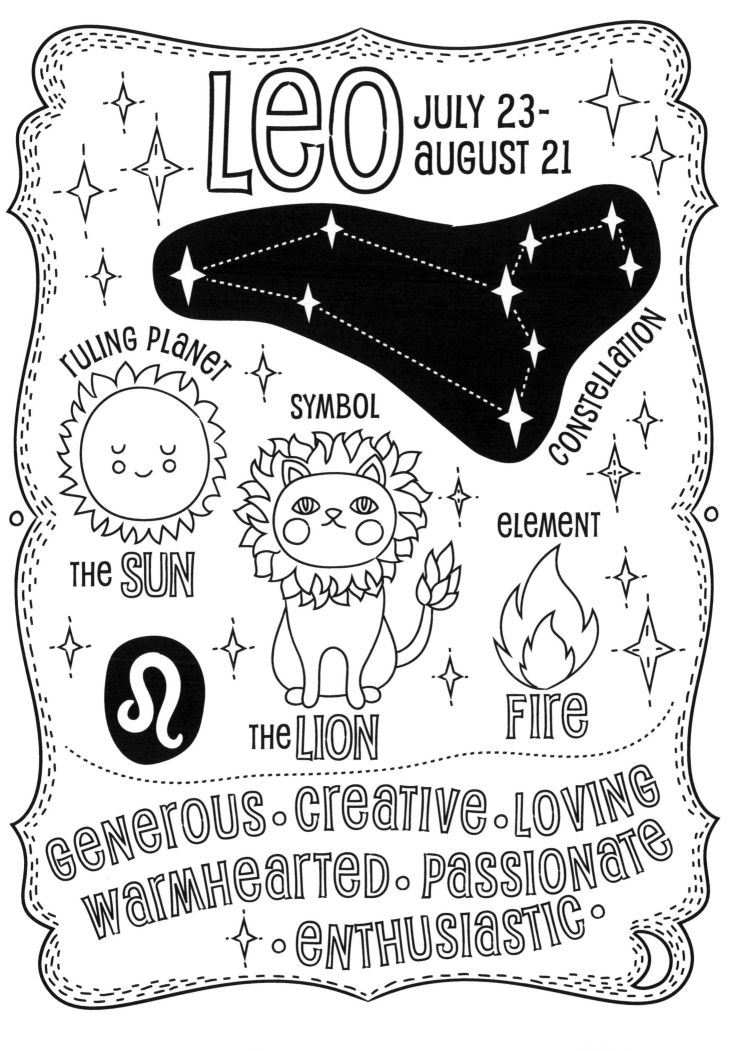

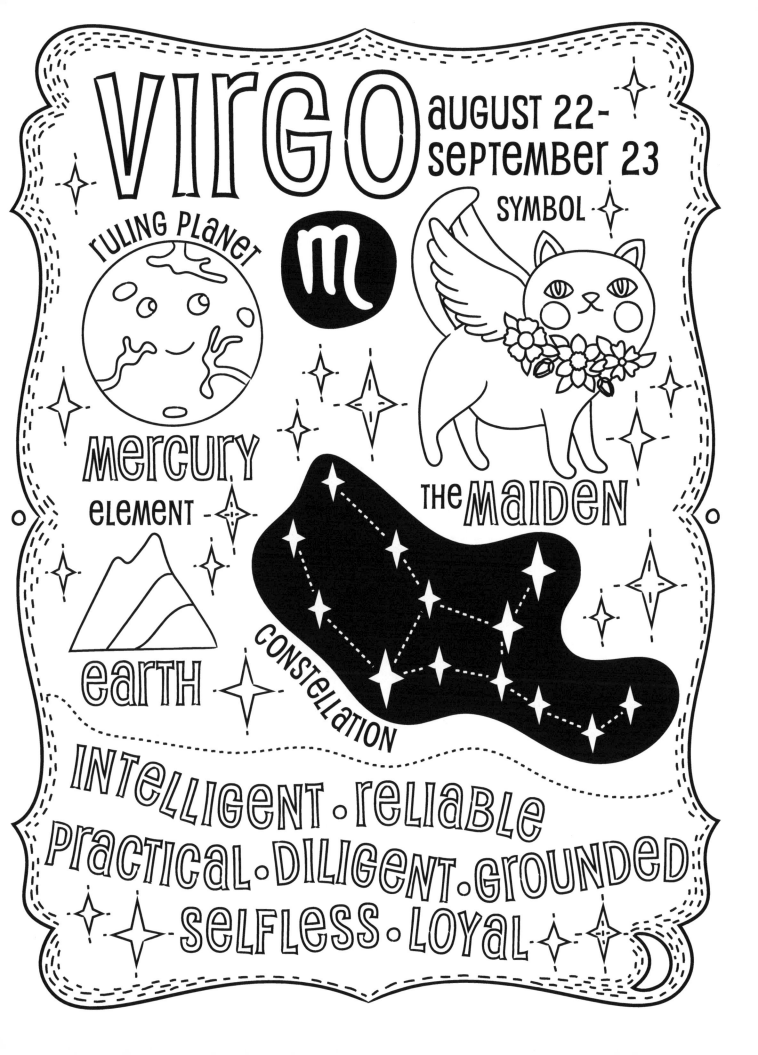

Made in the USA
Monee, IL
14 September 2020